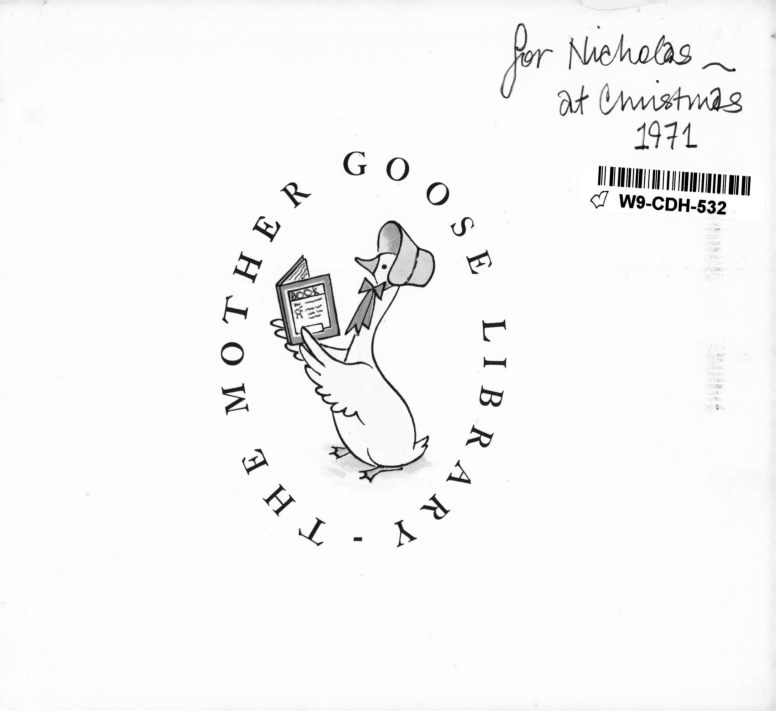

THE MOTHER GOOSE LIBRARY

To the memory of Seth M. Agnew

First published in Great Britain in 1969 by
World's Work Ltd, Kingswood, Tadworth, Surrey

Printed by offset in Great Britain by
William Clowes and Sons Ltd, London and Beccles

SBN 437 76503 2

Hurrah, We're Outward Bound!

Other books in The Mother Goose Library

LONDON BRIDGE IS FALLING DOWN!

TO MARKET! TO MARKET!

Far from home across the sea
To foreign parts I go;
When I am gone, O think of me
And I'll remember you.
Remember me when far away,
Whether asleep or awake,
Remember me on your wedding day
And send me a piece of your cake.

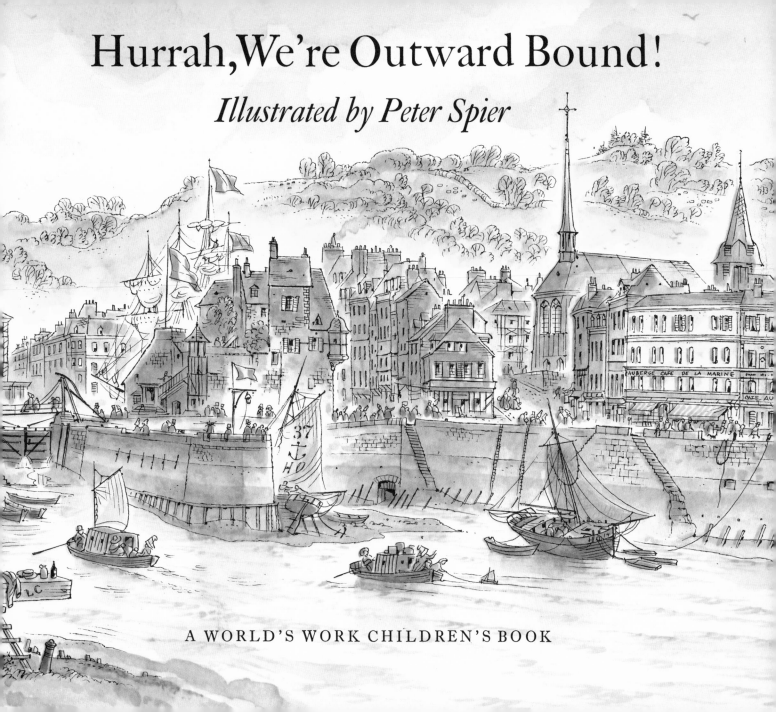

Hurrah, We're Outward Bound!

Illustrated by Peter Spier

A WORLD'S WORK CHILDREN'S BOOK

The water is wide, I can't get o'er. Neither I have the wings to fly.
Oh, go and get me a little boat, and we both shall row, my true love and I.

Oh, she was built in old Honfleur, built in the yard of Jacques le Coeur.
Away down the Seine she rolled one day, and across the Atlantic she ploughed her way.

Over the water and over the lea,
And over the water to Charley.
Charley loves good ale and wine,
And Charley loves good brandy,
And Charley loves a pretty girl
As sweet as sugar candy.

Over the water and over the lea,
And over the water to Charley.
I'll have none of your nasty beef,
Nor I'll have none of your barley;
But I'll have some of your very best flour
To make white cake for my Charley.

If all the world were paper,
And all the sea were ink,
If all the trees were bread and cheese,
What should we have to drink?

My mother sent me for some water,
For some water from the sea,
My foot slipped, and in I tumbled,
Three jolly sailors came to me:
One said he'd buy me silks and satins,
One said he'd buy me a guinea gold ring,
One said he'd buy me a silver cradle
For to rock my baby in.

There ain't but the one thing grieves my mind, to leave my wife and child behind.
My wife is standing on the quay; the tears do start as she waves to me.

O, fare you well, I wish you well! Goodbye, fare you well;
O, fare you well, my bonny young girls! Hoorah, my boys, we're outward bound!

Little ships must keep the shore; larger ships may venture more.

Sunday sail, never fail, Friday sail, ill luck and gale.

When sea birds fly to land,
A storm is at hand.

Mackerel skies and mares' tails
Make tall ships carry low sails.

Awake, awake, you weary sleepers,
Know you not 'tis almost day?
Here while thus you're sleeping,
God's best hours will pass away.
Show a leg! Show a leg!

The bo'sun shouts, the pumps stand by,
But we can never suck her dry.
Oh, heave around the pump-bowls bright:
There'll be no sleep for us tonight.

A Yankee ship came down the river,
Her masts and spars they shine like silver.
How do you know she's a Yankee liner?
The Stars and Stripes float out behind her.

Her sails were old, her timbers rotten,
His charts the skipper had forgotten.
She sailed away for London city;
Never got there, what a pity!

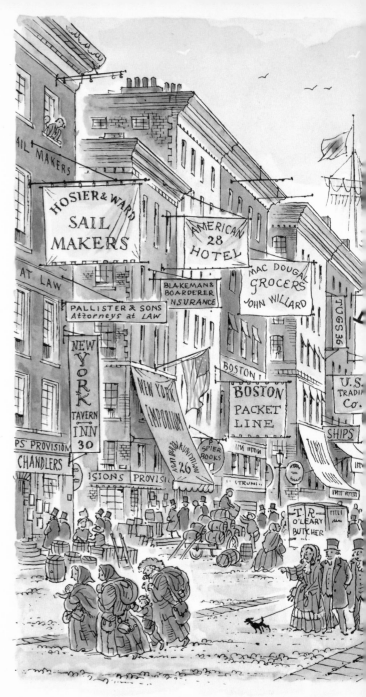

There is a ship that sails the sea.
She's loaded deep as deep can be,
But not so deep as the love I'm in.
I care not if I sink or swim.

To New York town we bid adieu,
To lovely Kate and pretty Sue;
Our anchor's weigh'd and our sails unfurl'd,
And we're bound to plough the wat'ry world,
And say we're outward bound,
Hurrah, we're outward bound!

Haul on the bow-line, our bully ship's a-rolling, haul on the bow-line, the bow-line *Haul!*
Haul on the bow-line, Kitty is my darlin', haul on the bow-line, Kitty lives at Liverpool,

Haul on the bow-line, the old man is growlin', haul on the bow-line, it's a far cry from payday,
Haul on the bow-line, so early in the morning.

There were three jovial Welshmen, as I have heard men say,
And they would go a-hunting upon St. David's day.

All the day they hunted and nothing they could find,
But a ship a-sailing, a-sailing with the wind.

I saw a ship a-sailing, a-sailing on the sea,

And oh but it was laden, with pretty things for thee.

She sells sea shells on the seashore;
The shells that she sells are sea shells I'm sure.
So if she sells sea shells on the seashore,
I'm sure that the shells are seashore shells.

As I walked out one sunny morn
To view the meadows round,
I spied a pretty primrose lass
Come tripping o'er the ground,
Singing blow, ye winds, in the morning,
Blow, ye winds, Hi! Ho!
Brush away the morning dew,
Blow, ye winds, Hi! Ho!

O Kitty Karson, jilted the parson, married a mason.

Parson Darby wore a black gown and every button cost half a crown;

O Nancy Dawson, she's got a notion, for our young bo'sun.

From port to port, and toe to toe, turn the ship and away we go!

The farmer's heart with joy is filled
When his crops are good and sound,
But who can feel the wild delight
Of the sailor home-ward bound?

But do not think our life is hard,
Though storms at sea mistreat us;
For coming home's a sweet reward,
When wives and sweethearts greet us.

Little drops of water,
Little grains of sand,
Make the mighty ocean
And the pleasant land.

"Honfleur has always been the dearest of my dreams," wrote the great French poet Baudelaire—whose mother lived there—around 1850, and it was also there that a group of young painters often met in the Inn of St. Simeon. Among them were Monet and Pisarro: the world was to know them as the "Impressionists."

The pictures in this book tell the story of the three-masted sailing ship *La Jeune Française*, built in Honfleur around 1830, and follow her on her maiden voyage to New York and home again by way of Dartmouth. Honfleur sits on the south shore where the river Seine flows into the English Channel. Across the river today is the great port of Le Havre, its sky dark from the smoke of factories and huge oil refineries—while Honfleur is a small and quiet monument to the past. But until the 18th century, when Honfleur lost her shipping and shipyards to Le Havre, this small town was an important port of long standing.

Honfleur first came to prominence as a fortified naval base in the Hundred Years' (1338-1453) War between France and England. The Vieux Basin was once a fortified harbour; ships can enter or leave it only at high tide through the two great lock doors, for at low tide there is no water outside, as you can see on the title page. The only part of the old fortifications remaining today is the Lieutenance, next to the basin's entrance, which for centuries was the residence of the King's lieutenant, or governor. During the Hundred Years' War, Honfleur was captured by the English, and one of its churches dates from that period: the church of St.

Etienne facing the old basin (in the picture where Charley shares with his girl "good ale and wine") was sponsored by Henry VI.

At the end of the war Honfleur lost its prominence as a naval fortress but prospered as a trading and fishing port. In many of the drawings you will see curious boat-shaped boxes: it is in these—then as now—that the newly caught, perishable shrimp are kept alive as they are towed home from the sea. Many buildings were constructed during this prosperous time. One of the first to go up after the English departed was Ste. Catherine's. Churches at that time were invariably built of stone, but it was impossible to find the architects and stonemasons to build a great new church as an offering to God for the end of the war. So Honfleur's shipwrights built twin-naved Ste. Catherine's in their own way: completely out of wood in the technical manner of a ship. Next to the church stands the famous bell tower. On the title page and in other pictures you can see it rising behind the old Auberge de la Marine, which is still a hotel, but today is called the Cheval Blanc.

During the 16th and 17th centuries Honfleur was the starting port for many explorers—among them Jacques Cartier, who left in 1534 to find a Northwest passage and found New France in Canada instead, and Samuel de Champlain, who sailed to Canada in 1608 and founded Quebec. Many expeditions to Brazil and the Indies left the old port, sailing down the Seine by the high bluff that is topped with the Chapel of Notre-Dame de Grâce. This chapel was built in 1613, replacing one built in 1023. *La Jeune*

Française put out to sea just past the chapel with the heartening thought, " Sunday sail, never fail."

After almost eight weeks *La Jeune Française* had crossed the Atlantic and reached New York with its cargo of wine and salt. Bo'sun Charley lost no time in taking a girl walking on Long Island to watch "A Yankee ship come down the river." Today he would be standing on the Promenade of Brooklyn Heights, looking across the East River at the skyline of New York City. Lower Manhattan was surrounded by countless wharves, and ships' bowsprits extended almost to the houses that lined the waterfront. When our ship left New York ("To New York town we bid adieu") it sailed past today's Battery Park. Originally built to defend the entrances to the Hudson and East rivers, it was at that time an amusement park.

After a rough crossing of two and a half months a landfall was made on the Devon coast. Water and provisions were needed, and the captain decided to put into Dartmouth. There Bo'sun Charley met the girl "selling sea shells on the seashore." The strange buildings on the left are "rope houses"—ships, no longer seaworthy, cut in half, set on end, and used for rope storage. The tall huts in the background are netting houses in which the fishing nets are hung to dry.

With Honfleur, Dartmouth shares a history of prominence and decline. As early as 1147 a great fleet took advantage of its sheltered deep-water harbour: the international fleet bound on the second Crusade. By the 14th century the town flourished with the wine trade from Bordeaux, but in 1453 England lost Bordeaux and Dartmouth lost her wine trade. Not much later French raiders began to harass the coast, and in 1481 the construction of Dartmouth Castle was begun to protect the harbour. We saw *La Jeune Française* (on the pages for "I saw a ship a-sailing") enter the Dart River past that same castle.

At the time of Elizabeth, Sir Walter Raleigh led several expeditions from Dartmouth, and in 1588 nine ships sailed from there and helped to defeat the Spanish Armada. It is said that some of the ancient, blackened beams in the Royal Castle Hotel came from an Armada galleon wrecked nearby. During the 17th century Dartmouth replaced her lost French wine trade with codfish and prospered again. During this period the very old St. Petrox Church was rebuilt to its present appearance as seen in the picture with Parson Darby watching the ship turn and go. It was also at this time that the little *Mayflower* put into Dartmouth Harbour for repairs before crossing the Atlantic to Plymouth, Massachusetts.

In Victorian times Dartmouth began its decline as a commercial port, and today it is a quiet haven for tourists and yachtsmen. It is also the home of the Royal Naval College. More than 800 years after the Crusaders' fleet assembled in Dartmouth, another mighty fleet gathered in the very same place: in June 1944 the American force—more than 600 ships—sailed from here for Arromanches, known by the code name Omaha Beach, in the invasion of Normandy.

All the pictures for this book were first sketched by Peter Spier in Normandy and Devon and from historical documents of early New York.

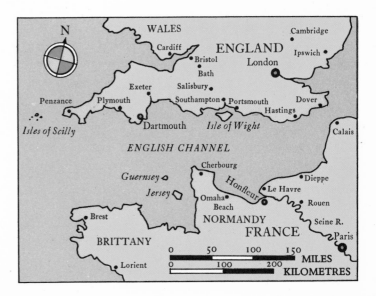

THE MOTHER GOOSE LIBRARY